4

SAUNDERS DECIDED TO LAY DOWN THE LAW, PRODDING BOB IN THE CHEST AS HE DID SO.

RIGHT, YOU LOT ARE ON A CHARGE. WE'LL START WITH BEING IMPROPERLY DRESSED . . .

UH-OH. THE POM SHOULDN'T HAVE DONE THAT.

THERE WAS A BRIEF SCUFFLE THAT WOULD END IN THE M.P. TAKING AN UNSCHEDULED SWIM.

YOU'D BETTER MAKE THAT RESISTING ARREST AS WELL, MATE.

AAGH!

THE SERGEANT HAD PICKED ON THE WRONG BLOKES TO NEEDLE, BUT THE INCIDENT WAS NOT OVER. A MILITARY POLICE OFFICER HAD SEEN IT ALL.

THOSE MEN THERE. STOP WHERE YOU ARE!

IS HE TALKING TO US, CORP?

IGNORE HIM. HE'S JUST A POM.

THE FOUR DIDN'T GET VERY FAR. FOREWARNED THAT THE AUSTRALIANS MIGHT CAUSE PROBLEMS, THE REDCAPS WERE OUT IN FORCE.

WHAT D'YOU RECKON, CORP?

I RECKON WE COULD SORT THIS MOB OUT, BUT WE DON'T WANT TO SPOIL OUR CHANCES OF GETTING GOOD CONDUCT STRIPES.

THE AUSSIES WERE PLACED UNDER CLOSE ARREST, AND RETURNED TO THEIR REGIMENT FOR DISCIPLINING. FORTUNATELY, THEIR COMPANY COMMANDER, MAJOR BILL BAXTER, WAS JUST LIKE THEM.

IT WAS AN ACCIDENT. THE SERGEANT TRIPPED AND . . . FELL, SIR.

LIKE THOSE FOUR COPPERS BACK IN SYDNEY? THEY ALSO TRIPPED AND FELL, DID THEY?

BAXTER SHOOK HIS HEAD IN DESPAIR. HE KNEW THAT ANY PUNISHMENT, SHORT OF THE FIRING SQUAD, WOULD BE WASTED ON THESE MEN. HE SHOULD HAVE CALLED FOR A COURT-MARTIAL, BUT HE KNEW BLOKES LIKE THIS WOULD BE NEEDED BEFORE LONG.

SEVEN DAYS RESTRICTED PRIVILEGES — MARCH THEM OUT, SERGEANT MAJOR.

OVER THE NEXT FEW DAYS, BOB AND HIS MATES DISCOVERED JUST HOW UNPREPARED SINGAPORE WAS. MOST OF THE HEAVY GUNS HAD BEEN POINTED OUT TO SEA, BUT THE ENEMY ATTACK WAS COMING FROM INLAND.

THAT'S TYPICAL. THEY FINALLY TURN THEM ROUND, BUT THEN THEY SEND THE WRONG AMMO.

IF THAT'S WHAT YOU POMS ARE LIKE, WE MIGHT AS WELL SHOW THE WHITE FLAG NOW.

THE ROYAL ARTILLERY CORPORAL TOOK EXCEPTION TO BOB'S REMARK.

WE WON'T BE NEEDING THESE GUNS. THOSE JAPS ARE USELESS AGAINST REAL TROOPS.

THAT'S WHAT THE YANKS THOUGHT, UNTIL THEY GOT CLOBBERED AT PEARL HARBOUR.

OVER THE NEXT FEW DAYS, THE FOUR AUSTRALIANS WERE APPALLED AT THE APPARENT COMPLACENCY THEY SAW AROUND THEM.

THE JAPS ARE COMING, AND THEY'RE ACTING AS THOUGH THIS IS A FLAMING HOLIDAY RESORT.

YEAH, WE'RE IN BIG TROUBLE.

BOB WAS RIGHT. IN THE MIDDLE OF FEBRUARY, THE ENEMY BROKE THROUGH THE DEFENSIVE CORDON AROUND THE TOWN.

THE AUSSIE REGIMENT HAD BEEN GIVEN THE TASK OF DEFENDING THE MAIN ROAD LEADING TO HEADQUARTERS. HEAVY SHELLING AND BOMBING CUT THE UNIT TO BITS.

AS MORE SHELLS BEGAN TO LAND, BOB LED THE WAY AS HE DUCKED INTO A LARGE HARDWARE SHOP.

STREWTH, THAT WAS A CLOSE ONE.

YEAH, THAT'LL SAVE 'EM HAVING TO CLEAN THOSE WINDOWS.

IN THE CELLAR THEY FOUND THE NERVOUS CHINESE OWNER OF THE STORE AND HIS ASSISTANT.

YOU GO QUICK. CAUSE NO TROUBLE.

WE INTEND TO, MATE. IS THERE A WAY OUT OF HERE?

THROUGH DOOR TO BACK-YARD. THERE YOU FIND MANHOLE LEADING TO SEWERS.

THE TOUGH FOURSOME MADE THEIR WAY ALONG THE STINKING SEWER WHICH TOOK THEM TO A BAY. FORTUNATELY THE TIDE WAS OUT.

WHAT NOW, CORP?

NOW WE FIND ANOTHER MOB TO JOIN. THERE'S STILL A WAR GOING ON.

BUT THEY WERE TOO LATE. REALISING THAT FURTHER RESISTANCE WAS FUTILE, THE DEFENDERS HAD BEEN ORDERED TO SURRENDER.

STREWTH, MATE. IT LOOKS LIKE THEY'VE THROWN IN THE BLASTED TOWEL.

THEY'RE FLAMING POMS, MICK, WHAT D'YOU EXPECT?

AS THEY MADE THEIR WAY ALONG THE BEACH THEY CAME ACROSS A MIXED GROUP OF BRITISH SOLDIERS AND SAILORS PUSHING A LAUNCH TOWARDS THE WATER. AMONG THEM WAS STEVE SAUNDERS, THE MILITARY POLICE SERGEANT THEY HAD RUN ACROSS EARLIER.

WOULD YOU LADS LIKE A LIFT?

IT'S THAT POM COPPER WE CHUCKED IN THE SEA.

AND HE'S OFFERING TO HELP US. SO LET'S NOT LOOK A GIFT HORSE IN THE MOUTH.

CLEARLY IN THE CIRCUMSTANCES, THE M.P. DID NOT HOLD A GRUDGE. IT TURNED OUT THAT THE VESSEL HAD BEEN STORED IN A SHED, AND THE SERGEANT HAD DECIDED TO REQUISITION IT.

THE SAILORS RECKON WE CAN GET TO AUSTRALIA IN THIS THING.

THEN I HOPE YOU MAKE IT, SARGE. BUT WE GOT SOME UNFINISHED BUSINESS TO TAKE CARE OF.

THE SERGEANT FOUND HIMSELF LOOKING AT THE
GRIM AND DETERMINED BUSHMEN.

UNFINISHED
BUSINESS?

OUR REGIMENT
GOT WIPED OUT
BACK THERE, AND IT'S
UP TO US TO EVEN
THE SCORE.

SO IF
YOU'LL DROP
US OFF ALONG
THE COAST!
TA.

SELECTING AN AREA OF JUNGLE, THE BOAT CAME IN
CLOSE TO THE SHORE TO LET BOB AND HIS MEN OFF.

IT'S PRETTY
DANGEROUS IN
THERE.

DON'T WORRY,
SARGE. WE'RE USED TO
ROUGHING IT. IT'LL BE JUST
LIKE A SUNDAY STROLL
THROUGH THE PARK.

BUT ANY CONFIDENCE PROVED TO BE MISPLACED WHEN THEY FOUND
HOW HARD THE GOING WAS THROUGH THE JUNGLE.

PHEW. IT'S LIKE
A FLAMING TURKISH
BATH IN HERE.

I DON'T KNOW
ABOUT YOU BLOKES,
BUT THESE CREEPERS
ARE BEGINNING TO
ANNOY ME.

BUT, AS THE DAYS PASSED, THEIR SPIRITS
BEGAN TO RISE AS THEY FOUND A
PLENTIFUL SUPPLY OF FOOD AND WATER.

ALMOST AS
GOOD AS THE BUSH
TUCKER BACK HOME.

HEY, CORP,
HOW MANY MILES
D'YOU RECKON
WE'VE COME?

BUT JUST THEN THEY HEARD THE
UNMISTAKABLE SOUND OF A RIFLE SHOT.

I BET
THAT'S NOT
FRIENDLY. IT CAME
FROM OVER
THERE.

A FEW MOMENTS LATER, A NATIVE BURST OUT OF THE UNDERGROWTH, RUNNING PAST THEIR POSITION AT TOP SPEED.

STREWTH, THAT BLOKE'S IN A HURRY.

YEAH, IT LOOKS LIKE HE COULD USE SOME HELP.

BOB WAS RIGHT. FOR THE MAN WAS BEING PURSUED BY A JAP PATROL LED BY A SERGEANT-MAJOR.

HE CAN'T BE FAR AWAY, SIR.

AND WHEN WE CATCH HIM, HE WILL DIE SLOWLY.

MOMENTS LATER, THE ENEMY WERE CAUGHT IN A HAIL OF BULLETS FROM BOTH SIDES OF THE CLEARING AS BOB RAPPED OUT AN ORDER.

LET THOSE DRONGOS HAVE IT.

URRGH!

AGGGH!

THE RUNNING MAN RETURNED TO FIND ALL THE JAPS WIPED OUT.

IT'S THAT SPRINTER BLOKE . . .

PITY HE DOESN'T TALK ENGLISH. I'D LIKE TO KNOW WHY THESE JAPS WERE CHASING HIM.

THE NATIVE SMILED, INTRODUCING HIMSELF AS TONGO.

THEY SHOOT BECAUSE I JOLLY WELL UPSET THEM. I KILL ONE WITH BOW AND ARROW LIKE ROBIN HOOD.

STREWTH, HE DOES TALK ENGLISH.

TONGO EXPLAINED THAT THE JAPS HAD TRESPASSED ON HIS TRIBE'S HUNTING GROUNDS AND KILLED ONE OF THEIR PIGS.

URGH!

AMBUSH!

A WELL-AIMED ARROW FROM TONGO TOOK REVENGE.

THESE TRIBESMEN WERE CLEARLY AGGRESSIVE. THAT GAVE THE AUSSIES AN IDEA.

A BOW AND ARROW, EH? JUST THINK WHAT THEY COULD DO WITH THESE JAP RIFLES.

ARE YOU THINKING WHAT I'M THINKING?

I RECKON WE COULD ORGANISE THESE FELLERS INTO A FAIR DINKUM RESISTANCE GROUP.

GATHERING UP THE ENEMY WEAPONS, BOB ASKED TONGO TO TAKE THEM TO HIS VILLAGE.

YOU TALK JUST LIKE AN UPPER CLASS POM. WHERE DID YOU LEARN ENGLISH, MATE?

GOOD OLD BISHOP TAUGHT US. HE'S A JOLLY FINE FELLOW.

THE AUSTRALIANS AUTOMATICALLY ASSUMED TONGO WAS TALKING ABOUT A MISSIONARY.

A BISHOP, EH? SOME MISSION SCHOOL, I BET.

WE'D BETTER WATCH OUR LANGUAGE, CORP.

WE'LL SEND HIM PACKING. THIS IS NO PLACE FOR A MAN OF THE CLOTH.

AS THEY ARRIVED AT THE VILLAGE, THEY WERE GREETED BY THE CHIEF, WHO WAS ACCOMPANIED BY A YOUNG MAN WEARING CRUMPLED CIVILIAN CLOTHES AND THE THICKEST LENSES IN ANY GLASSES THAT THEY HAD EVER SEEN.

HARRY BISHOP'S THE NAME. AND WHO MIGHT YOU CHAPS BE?

AUSSIES TO A MAN.

HE DON'T LOOK LIKE A CLERGYMAN TO ME.

FOR A MOMENT, HARRY LOOKED PUZZLED. BUT THEN HE CHUCKLED.

CLERGYMAN? OH, I SEE HOW YOU GOT THAT IDEA. BISHOP IS JUST MY NAME. ACTUALLY, I'M AN ENTOMOLOGIST.

ENTO-WHAT? SPEAK ENGLISH, MATE.

CLEARLY IRRITATED BY WHAT HE SAW AS THEIR IGNORANCE, HARRY EXPLAINED THAT HE STUDIED INSECTS. IN FACT, HE WAS LOOKING FOR A SPECIES OF BEETLE THOUGHT TO BE EXTINCT FOR OVER THOUSANDS OF YEARS.

I THINK I MAY HAVE LOCATED IT, THOUGH.

A BUG HUNTER, EH? BETTER YOU THAN ME. I HATE CREEPY-CRAWLIES.

AT THAT MOMENT, BOB SAW A BEETLE SCUTTLE PAST.

SO DO I — AND WHEN I SEE 'EM, I WANT TO SQUASH THEM.

NO! DON'T YOU DARE!

UH-OH. BAD MOVE!

CASEY KNEW HOW SHORT BOB'S TEMPER WAS. GRABBING HARRY BY THE SHIRT, THE N.C.O. LIFTED HIM OFF THE GROUND.

SO, YOU WANT TO FIGHT, EH? YOU SHOULD BE FIGHTING THE JAPS! DON'T YOU KNOW THERE'S A WAR ON?

PUT ME DOWN. YES, I HEARD SOMETHING ABOUT THAT . . .

THE NEXT MOMENT THE AUSSIES FOUND THEMSELVES SURROUNDED BY SOME ANGRY-LOOKING NATIVES WIELDING RAZOR-SHARP SPEARS.

PLEASE DO NOT HARM MISTER BISHOP — HE JOLLY NICE FELLOW.

I DON'T BELIEVE THIS.

BETTER DO WHAT HE SAYS, CORP. THEY LOOK LIKE THEY MEAN IT.

DROPPING THE BUG HUNTER IN DISGUST, BOB LED HIS MATES OUT OF THE VILLAGE.

COME ON, LADS. WE'LL FIND ANOTHER BUNCH TO TRAIN.

YEAH, THIS LOT CAN LOOK FOR BEETLES WHILE WE DO MORE IMPORTANT WORK.

THE ENEMY WEAPONS WERE CONCEALED NEARBY TO AWAIT LATER COLLECTION.

AS THEY MADE THEIR WAY THROUGH A RUBBER PLANTATION, THEY SAW A NOTICE PINNED TO ONE OF THE TREES. INFORMATION LEADING TO CAPTURE OF BRITISH AND AUSTRALIAN SOLDIERS WOULD BE REWARDED.

NICE OF 'EM TO PRINT IT IN ENGLISH, TOO.

YEAH, I RECKON I COULD RETIRE IF I GRASSED ON YOU BLUDGERS.

THE WANDERING AUSSIES ALSO SOON DISCOVERED THAT THE OTHER TRIBES IN THE AREA DIDN'T SEEM INTERESTED IN RESISTING THE JAPS.

CHIEF SAYS WE HAVE HAD INVADERS BEFORE. IN TIME, THE JAPANESE WILL LEAVE.

YEAH, BUT WE CAN'T WAIT THAT LONG.

WE'RE WASTING OUR TIME, CORP. LET'S GO.

BUT ONE OF THE VILLAGERS WAS DETERMINED TO CLAIM THAT REWARD AND IT WASN'T LONG BEFORE A JAP PATROL GOT THEM IN THEIR SIGHTS.

I RECKON SOME RAT'S BETRAYED US, MATE.

FLAMING NORA! WHAT ELSE CAN GO WRONG?

THEY WERE ABOUT TO FIND OUT. THE NEXT MOMENT, THEY FOUND THEMSELVES STANDING IN FRONT OF A STEEP DROP.

ANY TEMPTATION TO HESITATE WAS QUICKLY OVERCOME BY THE SOUND OF BULLETS WHISTLING OVER THEIR HEADS. THEY LEAPT INTO SPACE.

THE NEXT MORNING, TONGO WAS OUT HUNTING. HE GOT THE SHOCK OF HIS LIFE WHEN THE AUSSIES STAGGERED OUT OF THE UNDERGROWTH.

OH, MY GOSH. WHAT HAPPEN TO YOU GENTS?

WE WERE PRACTISING OUR PARACHUTE JUMPS.

JUST A PRIVATE JOKE, MATE.

TONGO TALKED THEM INTO COMING BACK TO THE VILLAGE TO AT LEAST REST, BUT, WHEN THEY GOT THERE THEY FOUND THE NATIVES IN A STATE OF PANIC.

OUR SCOUT REPORTS MANY OF JAPANESE HEADING THIS WAY.

ONE OF THOSE BLUDGERS WE AMBUSHED TWO DAYS AGO MUST HAVE GOT AWAY.

IT WAS OBVIOUS THE ENEMY WOULD BE OUT FOR BLOOD, SO BOB KNEW THEY HAD TO ACT FAST.

MATE, GET YOUR WOMEN AND CHILDREN TO NEARBY VILLAGES. THEN WE NEED A GOOD HIDEOUT.

I KNOW A PLACE.

TONGO POINTED INTO THE JUNGLE, EXPLAINING THAT THERE WAS AN OLD TEMPLE IN THE MIDDLE OF A BIG SWAMP.

PLENTY DANGEROUS. LOTS OF NASTY SNAKES AND INSECTS, BUT MISTER BISHOP FIND A WAY IN.

THEN HE CAN LEAD THE WAY.

BOB REALISED THAT HARRY MIGHT JUST PROVE USEFUL AFTER ALL, BUT TONGO SHOOK HIS HEAD.

HE NOT HERE. HE OUT LOOKING FOR INSECTS.

THEN WE'D BETTER FIND THE BLUDGER BEFORE THE JAPS DO.

ORDERING HIS MATES TO HAND OUT THE CAPTURED JAP WEAPONS WHICH THE AUSSIES HAD HIDDEN AWAY EARLIER, BOB TURNED TO THE CHIEF.

SET FIRE TO THE VILLAGE AND LEAVE NOTHING FOR THE JAPS. THEN MEET US AT THE SWAMP, BUT COVER YOUR TRACKS.

IT SHALL BE DONE, OLD BEAN.

AT THAT MOMENT, TWO MILES AWAY, HARRY BISHOP WAS WITNESSING ANOTHER CONFLICT — ONE BETWEEN SCORPIONS.

TWO PERFECT SPECIMENS OF THE GENUS HYPOCTONUS. HELLO?

HARRY'S EARS HAD BECOME ULTRA-SENSITIVE TO THE SOUNDS OF THE JUNGLE.

SOMEONE'S COMING, AND BY THE WAY THEY'RE TRAMPING THROUGH THE UNDERGROWTH, IT COULD BE THOSE ROUGH AUSTRALIANS.

BUT THE SOLDIERS WHO APPEARED WERE INHABITANTS OF A LESS-FRIENDLY ISLAND — JAPAN.

HANDS UP — SPEEDO!

THESE BLIGHTERS LOOK DECIDEDLY NASTY.

AS HARRY TOOK TO HIS HEELS, THE JAPS WERE ABOUT TO OPEN FIRE WHEN A MILITARY INTELLIGENCE CAPTAIN CALLED YAMAMURA APPEARED.

DON'T SHOOT! I WANT HIM ALIVE!

YES, SIR.

BUT, WHILE THE ENEMY WERE STRANGERS TO THIS JUNGLE, HARRY KNEW EVERY TRAIL LIKE THE BACK OF HIS HAND. HE HAD SOON BUILT UP A GOOD LEAD ON HIS PURSUERS.

I'D BETTER GET BACK AND WARN THE CHIEF.

HE MIGHT HAVE MADE IT IF HE HADN'T STEPPED INTO AN ANIMAL TRAP LAID BY ONE OF THE NATIVES AND FOUND HIMSELF SWUNG VIOLENTLY INTO THE AIR.

OH, GOSH!

HE HUNG THERE HELPLESS LIKE A HUMAN PENDULUM UNTIL THE JAPS FINALLY FOUND HIM.

THEY REGARDED THEIR CAPTIVE WITH AMUSEMENT.

HE LOOKS LIKE A CIVILIAN, SIR.

IN THAT CASE, HE MUST BE A SPY. WE WILL TAKE HIM BACK FOR INTERROGATION.

MASKED BY THE DEEP COVER OF THE JUNGLE, BOB AND TONGO ARRIVED JUST IN TIME TO SEE HARRY BEING CUT DOWN.

WE'RE TOO FLAMING LATE. THE NIPS HAVE GOT HIM.

FOR A BRIEF MOMENT THE AUSSIE WAS TEMPTED TO LEAVE HARRY TO HIS FATE, BUT HE SAW HOW WORRIED TONGO WAS.

TELL ME HOW TO GET TO THE SWAMP, THEN YOU FOLLOW THOSE JAPS AND FIND OUT WHERE THEY'RE TAKING HIM.

WILL DO, OLD CHAP.

WHEN BOB RENDEZVOUSED WITH HIS MATES AND THE ABLE-BODIED VILLAGERS ON THE EDGE OF THE SWAMP, THE AUSSIES WERE NOT VERY IMPRESSED.

STREWTH, IT STINKS.

YEAH, IT'S ALMOST AS BAD AS YOUR SOCKS.

STOP WHINGING. WE'VE GOT WORK TO DO.

CALLING THE CHIEF OVER, BOB OUTLINED HIS PLAN OF ACTION.

WE'VE ONLY GOT ENOUGH AMMO TO TRAIN ONE OF YOUR MEN TO USE A RIFLE, SO WHO'S YOUR BEST SHOT?

I SHOW YOU, OLD BEAN.

TO BOB'S DELIGHT, THE CHOSEN NATIVE TOOK TO RIFLE SHOOTING LIKE A DUCK TOOK TO WATER, HITTING HANGING GOURDS EVERY TIME.

BONZER SHOT, MATE.

IT'S ALL DOWN TO TONGO NOW. LET'S HOPE HE MANAGES TO LOCATE THAT FLAMING BUG HUNTER.

MEANWHILE, TONGO HAD TRACKED HARRY AND HIS CAPTORS TO AN INTELLIGENCE UNIT LOCATED ON A LARGE RUBBER PLANTATION.

IF THEY HURT MISTER BISHOP, THEY WILL PAY FOR IT.

TO HELP SOFTEN HARRY UP, YAMAMURA LET HIM STEW FOR FORTY-EIGHT HOURS BEFORE BEGINNING THE INTERROGATION.

I AM CAPTAIN YAMAMURA OF THE IMPERIAL ARMY.

HARRY BISHOP OF THE ROYAL ENTOMOLOGICAL SOCIETY. PLEASED TO MEET YOU, OLD CHAP.

JUST THEN THE ENEMY OFFICER SPOTTED A FLY ON THE TABLE AND SWATTED IT INSTANTLY — TO HARRY'S ANNOYANCE.

I SAY, THERE WAS NO NEED FOR THAT.

IT WAS DIRTY AND DISGUSTING!

NEXT, HARRY WAS TIED ROUGHLY TO A CHAIR.

YOU MUST BE ONE OF THESE ECCENTRIC ENGLISHMEN WE HAVE HEARD ABOUT.

I'M AN ENTOMOLOGIST AND I RESPECT ALL INSECTS, EVEN MEMBERS OF THE HUMBLE MUSCA FAMILY.

THE BUG HUNTER'S STORY THAT HE STUDIED INSECTS AND WASN'T VERY SURE ABOUT BRITAIN BEING AT WAR WITH JAPAN CUT NO ICE WITH HIS INTERROGATOR.

LIES! DO YOU TAKE ME FOR A FOOL?

IT'S THE TRUTH. AND, IF I CAN PROVE THE BEETLE I'M LOOKING FOR STILL EXISTS, I'LL BE VERY FAMOUS.

BY NOW, TONGO WAS LEADING THE RESCUE PARTY ALONG CONCEALED PATHS.

I DON'T FANCY BEING IN JAP HANDS.

THEY MAKE THE SPANISH INQUISITION LOOK LIKE SAINTS.

PHIL'S JOKE WASN'T TOO FAR OFF THE MARK. THE JAPS WERE TURNING ON THE PRESSURE, AND HARRY WAS TALKING AFTER BEING BEATEN.

COLEOPTERA, DERMAPTERA, DICTYOPTERA, DIPTERIA . . .

ARE YOU GETTING THIS DOWN?

YES, SIR — THEY MUST BE CODE WORDS.

RECITING THE NAMES OF EVERY BUG HE COULD THINK OF HAD BOUGHT HARRY TIME. HE WAS FINALLY ALLOWED TO REST.

WE WILL TALK AGAIN WHEN OUR CODE-BREAKERS HAVE DONE THEIR WORK.

I HOPE THAT TAKES LONG ENOUGH.

HARRY WAS LOCKED BACK IN HIS CELL AND, LATER THAT NIGHT, BRIGHT LIGHTS SUDDENLY FLARED IN THE NIGHT AS TWO ENEMY OFFICERS STROLLED FROM THEIR MESS.

I DON'T KNOW . . .

WHAT ARE THEY?

BUT THEY SOON REALISED THAT THE "LIGHTS" WERE COMING CLOSER AND PROVED TO BE CRUDE BUT EFFECTIVE FIRE-ARROWS.

SOUND THE ALARM. WE'RE UNDER ATTACK!

TWO TRUCKS PARKED BEHIND THE BUILDINGS HAD ALSO COME UNDER ATTACK FROM FLAMING ARROWS. AS THEIR FUEL TANKS EXPLODED, THEY ADDED TO THE CONFUSION.

GET ME BATTALION H.Q.!

THE PHONE LINES ARE DEAD, SIR.

THE ARROWS WERE SOON FOLLOWED BY SOME HIGHLY ACCURATE SMALL ARMS FIRE WHICH SAW EVEN YAMAMURA DUCKING.

THIS PROVES THAT ENGLISHMAN MUST BE A VERY IMPORTANT SPY. WE CANNOT AFFORD TO LOSE HIM.

TAKING NO CHANCES, THE OFFICER HAD THE PRISONER SEIZED BY TWO OF HIS MEN AND BUNDLED TO A STAFF CAR. YAMAMURA PAUSED ONLY LONG ENOUGH TO LEAVE HIS LIEUTENANT IN CHARGE.

IF THE ENEMY LOOK LIKE GETTING THROUGH, YOU MUST DESTROY ALL DOCUMENTS AND CODE BOOKS.

YES, SIR, UNDERSTOOD, SIR.

AS THE VEHICLE SPED AWAY AT TOP SPEED, YAMAMURA SNEERED AT HARRY WITH MALICE IN HIS EYES.

DO NOT THINK YOUR FRIENDS WILL RESCUE YOU.

LOOK, I'M A BLASTED ENTOMOLOGIST, NOT A SPY!

THEY DIDN'T GET FAR, THOUGH. A FEW MOMENTS LATER, THEY RAN INTO A BOOBY-TRAP MADE OF HEAVY BRANCHES WHICH SPORTED TOUGH THORNS.

I CAN'T HOLD IT!

THEY WON'T TAKE YOU BACK ALIVE, BISHOP!

AS YAMAMURA DREW HIS PISTOL AND FIRED, THE CAR SWUNG VIOLENTLY, CAUSING THE BULLET TO MISS AND GIVING HARRY THE CHANCE TO SOCK THE CAPTAIN.

AFTER THAT, THINGS MOVED QUICKLY AS THE VEHICLE TOPPLED OVER. WHEN IT ROLLED TO A STOP, THE DOOR WAS WRENCHED OPEN AND HARRY WAS DRAGGED OUT BY BOB.

MORE JAPS BEGAN TO CLOSE IN, SO THE FUGITIVES FLED THE SCENE. IT WAS LATER THE NEXT DAY THAT THE RESCUE PARTY FINALLY ARRIVED AT THE SWAMP.

YOU ARE SAFE, OLD CHAP.

A BIT BATTERED AND BRUISED. I COULD DO WITH A NICE HOT BATH AND A GOOD NIGHT'S SLEEP, CHIEF.

COULDN'T WE ALL, BUT FIRST YOU HAVE TO LEAD US TO THE TEMPLE.

AFTER ALL, THAT WAS WHAT THEY'D RESCUED HIM FOR, SO OFF THEY SET. MICK AND TONGO, GUARDING ONE FLANK, SOON DISCOVERED THE DANGERS.

MIND YOUR HEAD — THAT'S A WASPS' NEST.

BUZZING AWAY LIKE BLAZES THEY ARE TOO!

WHEN THEY REGROUPED FURTHER ON, THEY GAZED IN AWE AS HARRY POINTED TO SOME MORE OF THE OBJECTS HANGING FROM THE TREES.

YOU SHOULD SEE THE SIZE OF THESE WASPS. THEY SAY THEY CAN KILL A MAN IN FIVE MINUTES.

I'LL TAKE YOUR WORD FOR IT.

TEN MINUTES LATER, IT WAS PHIL'S TURN TO FALL FOUL OF THEIR SURROUNDINGS WHEN HE LOST HIS FOOTING AND SLIPPED INTO SOFT MUD.

AAGH!

CLUMSY CLOT — I TOLD YOU CHAPS TO WATCH YOUR STEP.

TONGO WATCHED IN ALARM AS BOB AND CASEY RUSHED OVER TO PULL PHIL OUT.

BETTER GET HIM OUT PRETTY QUICK. IF HE GET STUCK, HE WILL DROWN FOR SURE.

MEANWHILE YAMAMURA HAD SURVIVED THE CRASH BUT WAS STILL NURSING A SORE JAW AS HE FACED THE WRATH OF HIS SUPERIOR OFFICER.

TOKYO HAVE RETURNED THIS REPORT OF YOURS.

SOMETHING WRONG, COLONEL?

THE COLONEL COULD BARELY CONTAIN HIS ANGER. THE LIST HAD BEEN FOUND TO CONTAIN ONLY LATIN INSECT NAMES.

THIS ENGLISHMAN HAS MADE A COMPLETE FOOL OUT OF YOU AND THE PROUD JAPANESE ARMY!

ALTHOUGH THEY KEPT THEIR FACES BLANK, YAMAMURA KNEW THAT THE STAFF IN THE OUTER ROOM HAD OVERHEARD. THAT ONLY ADDED TO HIS HUMILIATION.

I MUST RESTORE MY HONOUR OR FACE THE CONSEQUENCES.

A WEEK LATER, AT A SMALL JAP LOOK-OUT POST GUARDING A MAIN ROAD THROUGH THE JUNGLE . . .

THERE IS LITTLE GLORY TO BE HAD OUT HERE.

WE CAN'T ALL BE HEROES, MY FRIEND.

THE TWO JAPS DIDN'T HEAR THE TWO ARROWS AS THEY FLEW THROUGH THE AIR. NEITHER DID THEIR COMRADES BELOW.

UGHH!

AGGHH!

A FEW SECONDS LATER, BOB EMERGED FROM THE JUNGLE AND MADE HIS WAY TO THE RAISED HUT BELOW THE TOP LEVEL.

THOSE BOWS ARE BONZER WEAPONS FOR A SILENT KILL.

THE CAPTURED JAP MACHINE-GUN WAS SOON PUT TO GOOD USE IN AN AMBUSH ON A SUPPLY TRUCK.

THEY NETTED SOME FOOD AND BOXES OF HAND GRENADES. THEY CARRIED THEIR LOOT BACK TO THE TEMPLE IN THE SWAMP WHICH THEY WERE NOW USING AS THEIR BASE.

DATUK BELONGED TO THE SAME TRIBE BUT HAD MOVED INTO THE TOWN. HE LOOKED WELL FED AND PROSPEROUS.

I OWN A SHOP NOW — A FAR CRY FROM HUNTING GAME WITH A BOW AND ARROW.

AS I RECALL, YOU WEREN'T VERY GOOD AT IT.

ALTHOUGH TONGO APPEARED FRIENDLY, HE HAD NEVER LIKED THE MAN.

YOU MUST COME TO MY HOUSE AND WE'LL TALK OF OLD TIMES.

I'D BETTER WATCH WHAT I SAY.

BUT AS THE PAIR CROSSED THE STREET, THEY WERE ALMOST RUN DOWN BY YAMAMURA'S CAR.

GET OUT OF THE WAY!

CURSED JAPANESE!

MAKING HIS EXCUSES, TONGO LEFT BUT KNEW THAT DATUK DID TRY TO FOLLOW HIM UNTIL HE LOST HIM.

THE ENEMY OFFICER HAD AN APPOINTMENT WITH A MALAYSIAN COLLABORATOR, A COLLEGE LECTURER WHO WAS AN EXPERT ON THE LOCAL TRIBES.

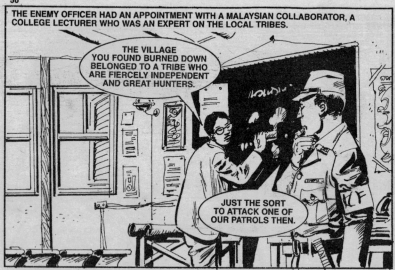

THE VILLAGE YOU FOUND BURNED DOWN BELONGED TO A TRIBE WHO ARE FIERCELY INDEPENDENT AND GREAT HUNTERS.

JUST THE SORT TO ATTACK ONE OF OUR PATROLS THEN.

SLOWLY BUT SURELY, YAMAMURA WAS BEGINNING TO BUILD UP A PICTURE OF THE PEOPLE WHO HAD CAUSED HIS LOSS OF FACE. THERE WAS ALSO A REPORT ABOUT FOUR AUSTRALIAN SOLDIERS SEEN IN THE AREA.

AND I'LL WAGER THEY'RE INVOLVED IN THIS AS WELL.

MEANWHILE, HARRY'S EXPERIENCE OF YAMAMURA'S HOSPITALITY HAD PERSUADED HIM TO TAKE A MORE ACTIVE ROLE IN THE WAR. HE LED BOB TO A SMALL CLEARING IN THE JUNGLE.

OKAY, WHAT IS IT YOU WANT TO SHOW ME?

SAY HELLO TO SOME FRIENDS OF MINE.

THINKING THAT THE BUG HUNTER MEANT EXOTIC CREEPY-CRAWLIES, BOB TURNED TO GO — BUT SUDDENLY A GROUP OF NATIVES APPEARED, AS IF BY MAGIC.

FLAMING NORA! WHERE DID THESE BLOKES COME FROM?

QUITE CLEVER WHAT? SEE HOW WELL THEY MERGE IN WITH THAT BODY PAINT?

AS THE AUSSIE WATCHED IN AMAZEMENT, THE NATIVES STEPPED BACK INTO THE UNDERGROWTH AND DISAPPEARED AGAIN ALMOST AT ONCE.

I GOT THE IDEA FROM INSECTS WHO USE NATURAL COLOURS TO CAMOUFLAGE THEMSELVES. THE PAINT COMES FROM BERRIES AND ROOTS.

MAYBE I'VE READ YOU WRONG, MATE.

BOB COULDN'T WAIT TO TEST OUT HIS NEW INVISIBLE ARMY ON THE ENEMY. THE FIRST PATROL TO COME ALONG WON THIS DUBIOUS PRIVILEGE.

I CAN'T STAND THIS HEAT.

BACK IN JAPAN, IT IS PROBABLY SNOWING.

FOR A MOMENT THE TWO SOLDIERS AT THE REAR WERE ABSORBED BY THOUGHTS OF THEIR HOMELAND. NEITHER HAD BEEN ON LEAVE FOR OVER A YEAR.

BUT THEY SAY THERE WILL BE A REWARD FOR THOSE MEN WHO FOUGHT IN SINGAPORE.

WHEN HE GOT NO REPLY, THE SOLDIER LOOKED BACK AND SAW THAT HIS MATE HAD DISAPPEARED.

THAT MEANS WE . . . TOSHIO? WHERE ARE YOU?

A MOMENT LATER, WHEN THE JAP WHO HAD BEEN THIRD FROM THE END, TURNED TO CHECK ON THE TWO AT THE REAR —

BY THE GODS — THEY'VE GONE!

WORD OF THE DISAPPEARANCES QUICKLY REACHED THE OFFICER LEADING THE SQUAD.

MAYBE THEY'VE DESERTED, SIR. PRIVATE HASEGAWA WAS ALWAYS COMPLAINING.

NO ONE DESERTS IN THE MIDDLE OF A JUNGLE! WE'LL SOON SORT THIS.

AS THE OFFICER WENT TO INVESTIGATE, A CAMOUFLAGED NATIVE REACHED FROM COVER TO SEIZE THE SERGEANT . . .

. . . WHO VANISHED WITHOUT TRACE, NEVER TO BE SEEN AGAIN.

THE NEXT MOMENT, MANY OF THE JAPS PANICKED AND BEGAN SHOOTING WILDLY IN ALL DIRECTIONS. THE CAMOUFLAGED STRIKE FORCE CREPT BACK TO JOIN THE OTHERS.

THEY'LL BE TELLING THEIR MATES THE JUNGLE IS HAUNTED.

YEAH, I RECKON WE'VE REALLY PUT THE WIND UP THOSE BLUDGERS.

BACK AT THE OLD TEMPLE RUINS, THEY WERE GREETED BY TONGO.

I HAVE MUCH TO REPORT, OLD BEAN.

OKAY, LET'S GO AND GRAB OURSELVES SOME TUCKER.

TONGO BRIEFED THEM ALL ABOUT HIS MISSION, AND WHEN DATUK'S NAME WAS MENTIONED, THE CHIEF SNORTED IN DISGUST.

PAH. I BANISHED THAT NO-GOOD ROTTER FOR STEALING.

DOES HE KNOW ABOUT THIS PLACE?

THERE WAS AN EMBARRASSED SILENCE WHICH HARRY FINALLY BROKE.

I FEAR SO, OLD BOY. IT WAS COMMON KNOWLEDGE.

THEN WE'D BETTER PRAY HE DOESN'T GO TO THE JAPS, EH, CORP?

WE CAN'T TAKE THAT CHANCE, PHIL. I RECKON THERE'S A GOOD CHANCE HE'S ALREADY DONE SO. THE CHIEF RECKONS HE'S A BAD 'UN.

ALL EYES WERE ON THE BUG HUNTER WHO DID NOT RELISH ANOTHER INTERVIEW WITH THE JAPANESE.

BUT, WITH A LITTLE ASSISTANCE FROM MY BUGS, I BELIEVE I CAN HELP DEFEND THIS PLACE.

MISTER BISHOP, HE GOOD EGG.

BOB KNEW THAT IF IT HADN'T BEEN FOR THE CAMOUFLAGE TRICK, HE WOULD PROBABLY HAVE REFUSED HARRY'S OFFER OF ASSISTANCE. MICK WASN'T SO SURE WHEN ALL THE NATIVES BEGAN COLLECTING CERTAIN LEAVES.

WHAT'S HE EXPECT US TO DO, CORP? DISGUISE OURSELVES AS FLAMING BUSHES?

LET'S WAIT AND SEE.

THEY WATCHED AS THE LEAVES WERE PLACED IN A LARGE POT AND BOILED WITH CAREFUL SUPERVISION BY HARRY.

ALL RIGHT, TONGO. I THINK IT'S READY.

HE'S A LUNATIC, THAT'S WHAT HE IS.

MAYBE WE WON'T NEED TO USE ANY OF THIS STUFF.

BUT THE UNTRUSTWORTHY DATUK HAD ALREADY REPORTED SEEING TONGO IN THE TOWN TO THE ENEMY AND WAS BEING MADE TO LEAD A FORCE OF JAPANESE COMMANDED BY YAMAMURA TOWARDS THE TEMPLE.

I COULD HAVE DRAWN YOU A MAP.

IF YOU WANT THAT REWARD MONEY YOU'LL HAVE TO EARN IT. YOU WILL TAKE US ALL THE WAY THERE.

WHEN ONE OF THE SCOUTS SPOTTED THEM, HE REPORTED STRAIGHT BACK TO THE CHIEF WHO SOUGHT OUT BOB AND HARRY.

JAPANESE ARE ABOUT THREE HOURS AWAY — THAT RASCAL DATUK LEAD THEM.

THEN WE'D BETTER GET CRACKING.

THE LEAVES THAT HAD BEEN PREPARED WERE NOW PUT TO GOOD USE, SMEARED ON THE BODIES OF SEVERAL OF THE NATIVES. THESE WARRIORS COULD NOW HIDE IN THE WORST OF THE SWAMP AND NOT BE STUNG OR BITTEN.

IT'S A SPECIAL RECIPE I CAME UP WITH TO KEEP THE LEECHES AND MOSQUITOES AT BAY.

I HATE TO ADMIT IT, BUT YOU'RE A FLAMING GENIUS.

IT HAD BEEN HARD WORK PREPARING FOR THE ATTACK, AND HARRY LOOKED WORRIED.

I WOULD HAVE LIKED TIME TO SET SOME MORE TRAPS.

THAT'S WAR FOR YOU, MATE. THINGS NEVER WORK OUT ACCORDING TO PLAN.

BUT THE NATIVES HAD OTHER IDEAS. HIDING IN THE REEDS, THEY USED THEIR BLOWPIPES TO FIRE DARTS AND BRING THE NESTS DOWN.

LOOK OUT!

RUN FOR YOUR LIVES!

PRETTY SOON THE AIR WAS FILLED WITH THOUSANDS OF ANGRY WASPS. ONLY YAMAMURA DID NOT GIVE IN TO THE FEAR AFFECTING HIS MEN.

AAGH!

COVER YOUR FACE AND DON'T PANIC!

DIVING INTO THE SWAMP WAS A FATAL MISTAKE, AS DATUK DISCOVERED WHEN HIS LEGS BECAME ENTANGLED IN THE WEEDS AND TONGO ROSE FROM COVER —

SAVE ME!

YOU WERE WILLING TO SELL US ALL FOR YOUR GREED, SO NOW YOU MUST PAY THE CONSEQUENCES!

A SPEAR WIELDED BY ANOTHER OF THE DEFENDERS DID FOR THE TRAITOR.

BY NOW EVEN YAMAMURA WAS GIVING WAY TO PANIC. USING HIS SHIRT TO COVER HIS FACE, HE TRIED TO IGNORE THE EXCRUCIATING PAIN AS HE PUSHED HIS WAY THROUGH MEN WRITHING IN AGONY.

AAIEE!

I MUST GET OUT OF HERE . . . AAGH!

AS THE OFFICER TRIED TO ESCAPE, HE HEARD THE CRIES OF HIS MEN AS THEY DROWNED IN THE SWAMP OR FELL VICTIM TO COUNTLESS VENOMOUS STINGS.

AAIEE!

I WILL NOT LET THEM GET THE BETTER OF ME.

BOB AND HARRY, HIDDEN AMONGST THE BUSHES, ARMED AND READY, SAW WHO WAS HEADING THEIR WAY.

THAT BRUTE OF AN OFFICER — HE'S MINE!

HARRY'S REVOLVER BARKED ONCE AND THE OFFICER DIED. IT WAS, IN FACT, A MERCY KILLING.

GOT HIM!

THAT'S PRETTY GOOD SHOOTING — FOR A BUG HUNTER!

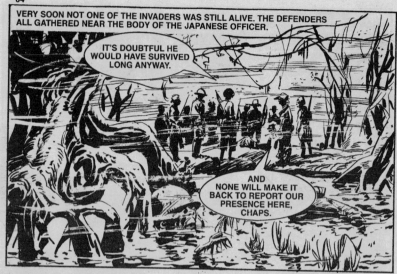

VERY SOON NOT ONE OF THE INVADERS WAS STILL ALIVE. THE DEFENDERS ALL GATHERED NEAR THE BODY OF THE JAPANESE OFFICER.

IT'S DOUBTFUL HE WOULD HAVE SURVIVED LONG ANYWAY.

AND NONE WILL MAKE IT BACK TO REPORT OUR PRESENCE HERE, CHAPS.

THAT NIGHT, THEY ALL CELEBRATED THEIR VICTORY WITH A BIG FEAST, AND THE AUSSIES HAD BEEN THINKING HARD.

MICK'S GOT A BONZER IDEA, CORP.

THE BUG HUNTER HERE COULD PUT THE WASPS TO SLEEP, AND WE COULD SNEAK THEIR NESTS INTO A JAP BARRACKS.

THEY'D BE OUR OWN MINIATURE AIR FORCE.

AFTER WHAT HAD HAPPENED TO YAMAMURA
AND HIS MEN, THE SWAMP GAINED AN EVEN
MORE SINISTER REPUTATION. AND THE JAPS
WERE FIRMLY CONVINCED THAT NO-ONE COULD
LIVE THERE. THIS GAVE BOB AND HIS MEN A
SECURE BASE, AIDED BY HARRY'S INSECT LORE.
AND, FOR THE DURATION OF THE WAR, HARRY'S
HUNT FOR THE ELUSIVE PREHISTORIC BEETLE
TOOK SECOND PLACE.

Commando
THE END

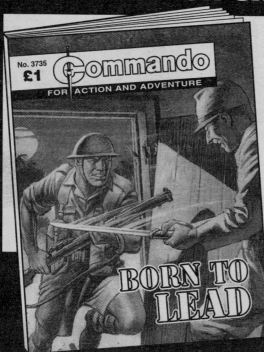
Printed and Published in Great Britain by D.C. THOMSON & CO., LTD.,
185 Fleet Street, London EC4A 2HS. © D.C. THOMSON & CO., LTD., 2004.